CW00349930

Tell the Time

How to use this book with your child:

It is recommended that an adult spends time with a child while doing any kind of school practice, to offer encouragement and guidance. Find a quiet place to work, preferably at a table, and encourage your child to hold his or her pen or pencil correctly.

Try to work at your child's pace and avoid spending too long on any one page or activity. Most of all, emphasise the fun element of what you are doing and enjoy this special and exciting time!

Don't forget to add your reward sticker to each page you complete!

Reward sticker!

Designed by Plum5
Illustrations by Sue King, Sharon Smart and Andy Geeson
Educational consultant Chris Andrew and Nina Filipek

www.autumnchildrensbooks.co.uk

Before or after?

Read the questions and label each picture with **before** or **after**.

a. Do you turn a tap on **before** or **after** you wash your hands?

b. Are you likely to wash the dishes **before** or **after** a meal?

Reward sticker!

Read the questions and label each picture with **before** or **after**.

c. Do you put a lead on a dog **before** or **after** you take it for a walk?

d. Do you cheer **before** or **after** someone scores a goal?

Reward sticker!

3

How long?

Time is measured in **seconds**, **minutes** and **hours**.

There are 60 **seconds** in one **minute**.

There are 60 **minutes** in one **hour**.

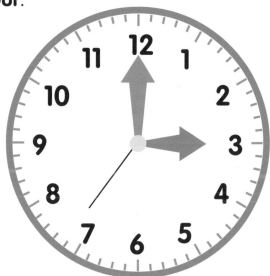

a. How long does it take to pick up a pen?
Circle the correct answer.

3 seconds   **3 minutes**   **3 hours**

Reward
sticker!

b. How long does it take to brush your teeth?
Circle the correct answer.

2 seconds   2 minutes   2 hours

c. How long does it take to watch a film?
Circle the correct answer.

2 seconds   2 minutes   2 hours

Reward
sticker!

Longest time

Look at these pictures carefully. Which do you think takes the longest amount of time? Place a ✔ in the box.

a.

doing a somersault

b.

climbing a mountain

Reward
sticker!

Which do you think takes the longest amount of time? Place a ✔ in the box.

a.

feeding the cat

b.

tidying your room

Reward sticker!

All at sea

Compare the pictures and look for the differences between day and night. Which picture is **day** and which is **night**? Write the correct answer in the box.

a.

b.

Reward sticker!

Puppy playmates

Compare the pictures and look for the differences between day and night. Which picture is **day** and which is **night**? Write the correct answer in the box.

a.

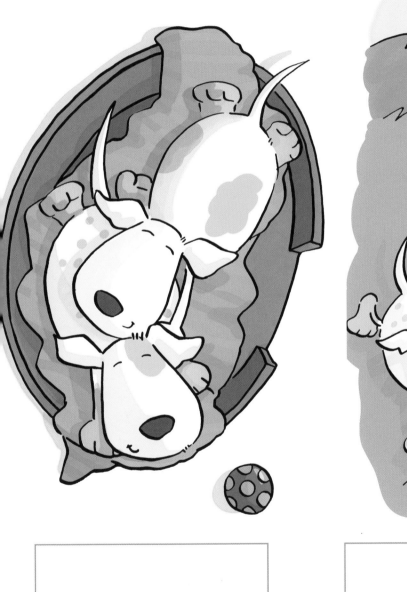

b.

Reward sticker!

Clock face

There are 12 numbers on a clock face. Use the numbers on this page to help you label the clock opposite. Write the numbers in the right squares. One has been done for you.

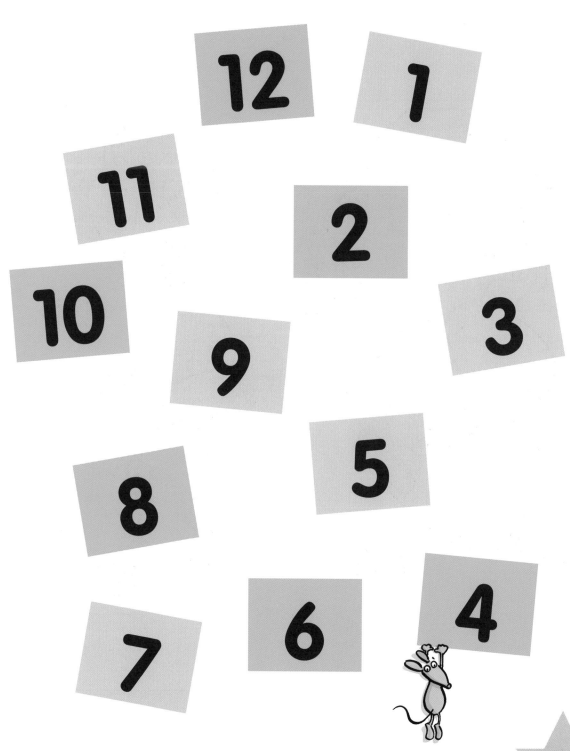

12

Reward sticker!

Clock hands

The hands on a clock face show you the time by pointing to numbers. The **short** hand points to the **hour**.
The **long** hand points to the **minutes**.

Reward
sticker!

Your turn

Using a ruler draw the short hand and point it to the number 9.
Then draw the long hand and point it to the number 12.
This shows you that it is 9 o'clock.

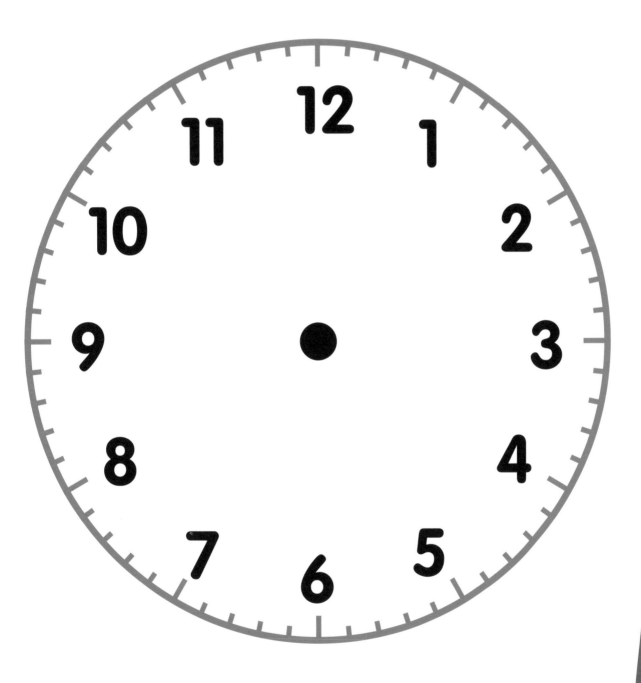

Reward
sticker!

Practice 1

Look at the times in the boxes under each clock. Draw hands on the clock faces so that they tell the times given in the boxes. Use the example to help you.

example

| 1 o'clock |

| 5 o'clock |

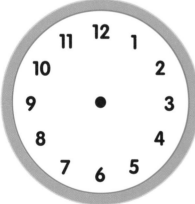

| 8 o'clock |

| 12 o'clock |

2 o'clock

4 o'clock

6 o'clock

7 o'clock

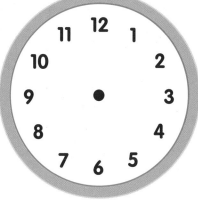

10 o'clock

What time of day?

Use the clues in the pictures to help you decide when these events most likely took place. Choose from the words on the opposite page and write the correct word in the boxes.

a.

b.

morning afternoon evening night

c.

d.

Reward
sticker!

17

Adding lots of 5

To count the number of minutes in an hour, go around the clock face and keep adding fives until you reach 60.
Finish writing the answers in the boxes.

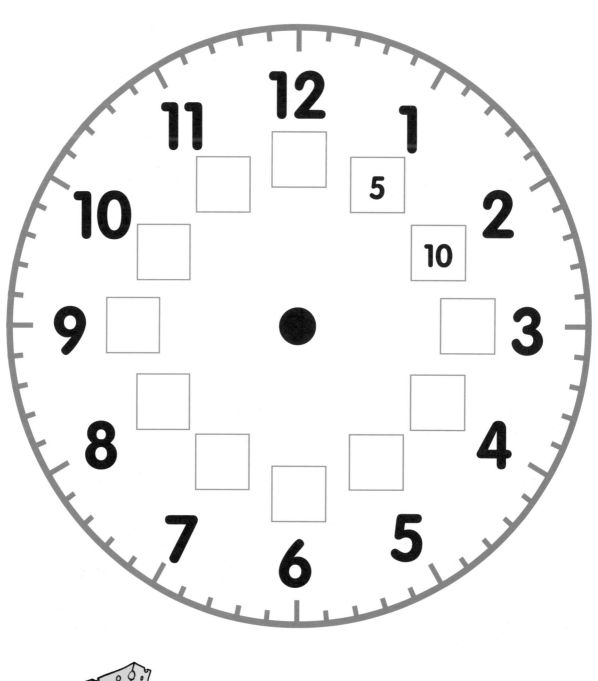

What's the time?

Match the times in the boxes to the times shown on each of these clocks by drawing a line to the correct time.

a.

12 o'clock

b.

5 o'clock

c.

7 o'clock

d.

8 o'clock

Reward sticker!

Half an hour

Like a pizza, a clock face can be cut into two halves or four quarters. There are **30 minutes** in half an hour.

2 halves

half an hour
(30 minutes)

Quarter of an hour

There are **15 minutes** in a quarter of an hour.

4 quarters

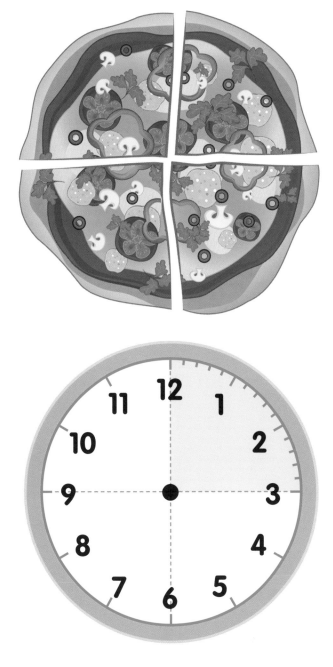

**quarter of an hour
(15 minutes)**

Half past

When the long hand points to the number 6, it is half past the hour.
Draw the long hand pointing to 6.
Then draw the short hand pointing halfway between 2 and 3.
This shows it is half past 2.

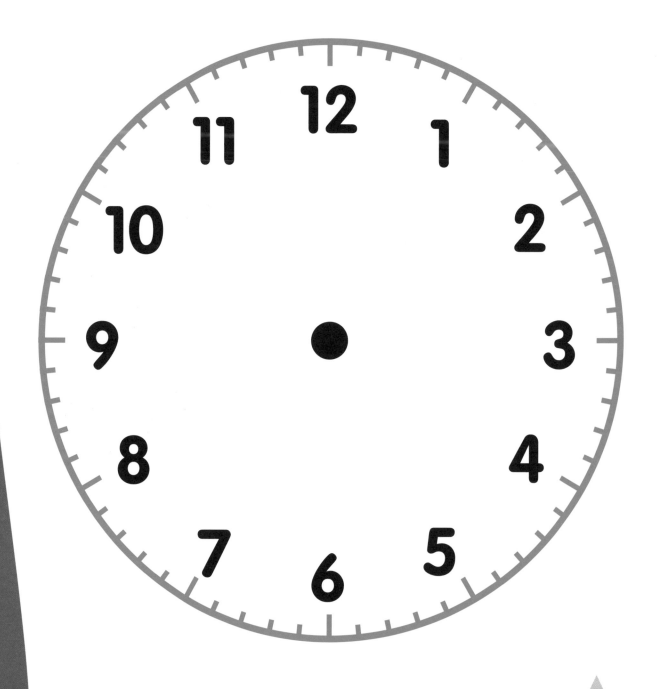

Reward sticker!

Quarter past

When the long hand points to the number 3, it is quarter past the hour. Draw the long hand pointing to 3.
Then draw the short hand pointing to just past 10.
This shows it is quarter past 10.

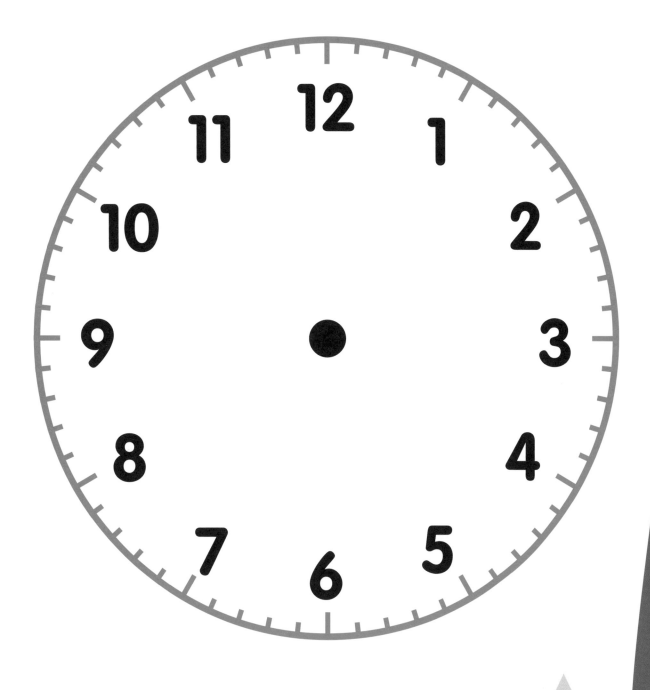

Quarter to

When the long hand points to the number 9, it is quarter to the hour. Draw the long hand pointing to 9.
Then draw the short hand pointing almost to 5.
This shows it is quarter to 5.

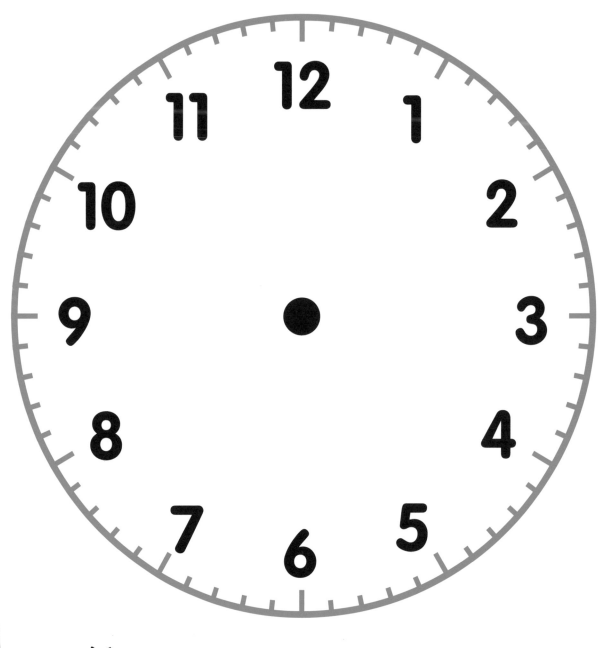

Reward sticker!

24

Practice 2

Look at the times on these clocks. Match the times in the boxes to the clocks by drawing a line to the correct time.

a.    b.    c.

| quarter to 4 | half past 3 | quarter past 2 |

Look at the times in the boxes.
Draw the missing hands on these clock faces.

d. 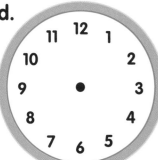   e.    f.

| half past 6 | quarter past 8 | quarter to 10 |

What time?

Look at the pictures and draw the missing hands on the clock beside each picture to show what time you might do these things.

Reward sticker!

Time for fun!

Reward
sticker!

27

Face to face

Look at the times in the boxes.
Draw the missing hands on these clock faces.

a.
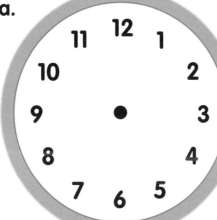

half past 2

b.
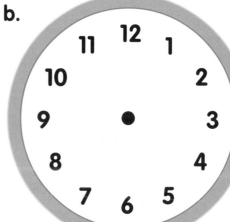

quarter to 8

c.
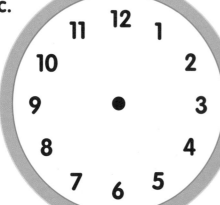

quarter past 7

d.
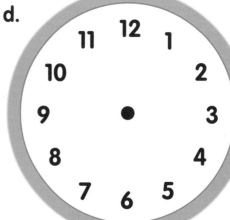

9 o'clock

Draw the hands

e.

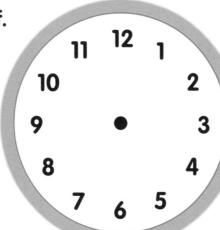

| quarter to 3 |

f.

| half past 10 |

g.

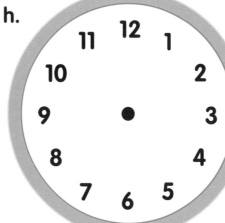

| quarter past 11 |

h.

| 5 o'clock |

24-hour clock

You have learnt that the hands on a 12-hour clock move around the clock face. After 12 o'clock midday, instead of starting again with 1 o'clock in the afternoon, a 24-hour clock shows 13:00.

So 2 o'clock in the afternoon is shown as 14:00, and so on.

The numbers change every minute up to 23:59 (1 minute before midnight). At midnight, a 24-hour clock shows 00:00, then starts again at 00:01 (1 minute past midnight).

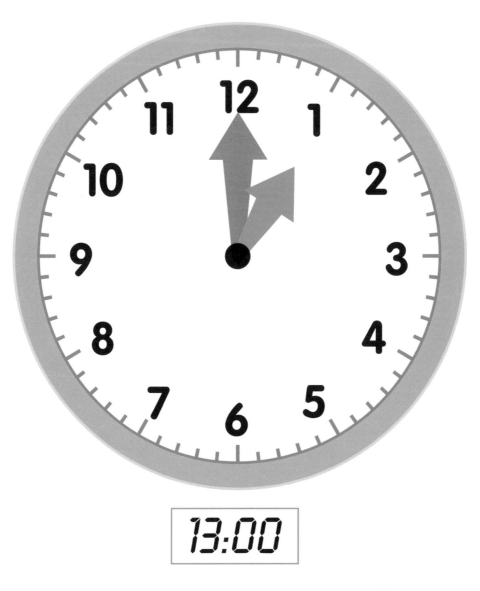

13:00

Reward sticker!

Practice 3

Look at the times on these 12-hour clock faces and match the same time on a 24-hour clock by drawing a line to the correct answer.

a.

b.

c.

14:00

15:00

13:00

Look at the times on these 24-hour clocks and draw the missing hands on the 12-hour clock faces to show the same time.

d.

e.

f.

16:00

17:00

18:00

Reward sticker!

Answers

Before or after?
a. before **b.** after **c.** before **d.** after

How long?
a. 3 seconds **b.** 2 minutes **c.** 2 hours

Longest time
Climbing a mountain takes the longest time.
Tidying your room takes the longest time.

All at sea
a. day **b.** night

Puppy playmates
a. night **b.** day

Clock hands

Practice 1

5 o'clock

8 o'clock

12 o'clock

2 o'clock

4 o'clock

6 o'clock

7 o'clock

10 o'clock

What time of day?
a. morning **b.** evening **c.** night **d.** afternoon

What's the time?
a. 8 o'clock **b.** 12 o'clock **c.** 5 o'clock
d. 7 o'clock

Half past

Quarter past

Quarter to

Practice 2
a. half past 3 **b.** quarter past 2 **c.** quarter to

d.

half past 6

e.

quarter past 8

f.

quarter to 10

Face to face

a.

half past 2

b.

quarter to 8

c.

quarter past

d.

9 o'clock

e.

quarter to 3

f.

half past 10

g.

quarter past 11

h.

5 o'clock

Practice 3
a. 13:00 **b.** 14:00 **c.** 15:00

d.

e.

f.